ISEB
Independent Schools
Examinations Board

SCIENCE
POCKET NOTES

David E Hanson
and
Katie Hanson

www.galorepark.co.uk

D0755921

ISEB
Independent Schools
Examinations Board

GALORE PARK

Published by ISEB Publications, an imprint of Galore Park
Publishing Ltd, 19/21 Sayers Lane, Tenterden, Kent TN30 6BW

www.galorepark.co.uk

Text copyright © David E Hanson and Katie Hanson 2006

Printed and bound in India by Replika Press Pvt. Ltd.

ISBN: 978 1 907047 12 1

First published 2009, reprinted 2010, 2012

Details of other ISEB revision guides, publications and
examination papers, and Galore Park publications are available
at www.galorepark.co.uk

Front cover image of a Timber Rattlesnake skeleton
Peter B Kaplan/Science Photo Library

CONTENTS

NOTE FROM THE AUTHORS

We hope that these notes may prove useful for those who readily forget, and serve as reminders in the final stages of preparation for examinations.

A few topics covered in this booklet are not in the current ISEB syllabus but have been included for general interest. These are marked with an asterix.

ACKNOWLEDGEMENT

We are grateful to Robert McVean, Headmaster of Aberlour House, the junior school at Gordonstoun, for reading and commenting upon the text, and to Sue Hunter for her help in proof-reading the material.

1. SCIENTIFIC ENQUIRY

1.1 USEFUL IDEAS AND EQUIPMENT

■ Data tables

animal study

animal	vertebrate	can fly
robin	y	y
mole	y	n
ladybird	n	y
woodlouse	n	n
salmon	y	n

height of plant

week	height, in cm
1	2
2	4
3	8
4	14
5	24

■ Sets

● Venn diagram

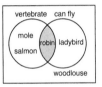

● Carroll diagram

invertebrate	ladybird	woodlouse
vertebrate	robin	mole salmon
	can fly	cannot fly

Note: each diagram has 4 regions.

■ Percentage and fraction diagrams

● pie chart

composition of Earth's atmosphere

nitrogen 78%
oxygen 21%
others 1%

● fraction diagram

composition of Earth's crust

oxygen 47%
silicon 28%
aluminium 8%
iron 5%
others 12%

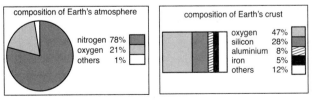

1

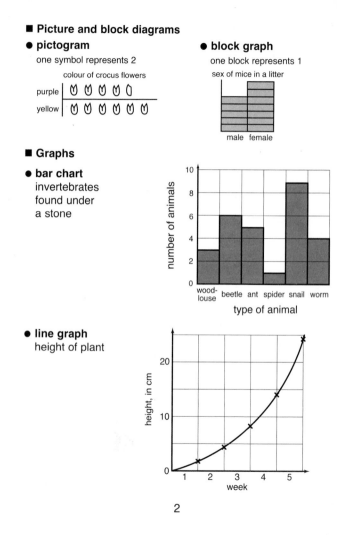

■ **Picture and block diagrams**

● **pictogram**

one symbol represents 2

colour of crocus flowers

purple | Ѱ Ѱ Ѱ Ѱ (

yellow | Ѱ Ѱ Ѱ Ѱ Ѱ Ѱ

● **block graph**

one block represents 1

sex of mice in a litter

male female

■ **Graphs**

● **bar chart**
invertebrates
found under
a stone

type of animal

● **line graph**
height of plant

week

2

- **frequency diagram**
  heights of seedlings

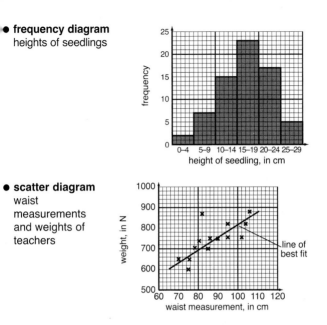

- **scatter diagram**
  waist
  measurements
  and weights of
  teachers

■ Flow charts

Consider using these when looking at

- physical changes
- chemical changes

- organism life cycles and natural (e.g. water) cycles

- food chains

■ Keys

Consider using these when identifying organisms or materials.

e.g. small invertebrate animals with legs

1	has fewer than 14 legs	→	go to 2
	has 14 or more legs	→	go to 3
2	has 6 legs, usually 3 clear body parts, sometimes wings	→	insect
	has 8 legs, usually 2 clear body parts, never wings	→	spider, mite
3	has 14 legs	→	woodlouse
	has more than 14 legs	→	go to 4
4	has 1 pair of legs on a body segment	→	centipede
	has 2 pairs of legs on a body segment	→	millipede

■ Scale drawings

● larger than life size

paramecium
(a single-celled organism)

100 : 1   10 000%   ×100

● smaller than life size

robin

1 : 8   12.5% $\times \frac{1}{8}$

4

■ Equipment

● **microscope**: used to magnify microscopic (very small) objects

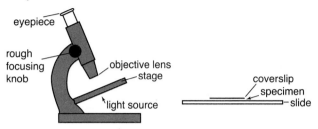

eyepiece

rough focusing knob

objective lens

stage

light source

coverslip
specimen
slide

a 10× eyepiece with a 40× objective lens gives a magnification of 400×(10×40)

● **quadrat**: a square frame (often with side 50 cm) used in organism population counts

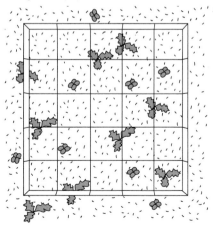

quadrat dropped at random (for example on a lawn when counting daisy and dandelion plants)

grid wires help in drawing a map showing positions of organisms

• bunsen burner

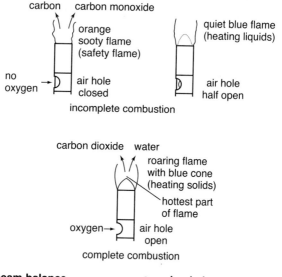

carbon   carbon monoxide

orange
sooty flame
(safety flame)

no
oxygen →   air hole
closed

incomplete combustion

quiet blue flame
(heating liquids)

air hole
half open

carbon dioxide   water

roaring flame
with blue cone
(heating solids)

hottest part
of flame

oxygen →   air hole
open

complete combustion

• beam balance
(compares masses)

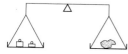

• spring balance
(measures downward pull of
gravity on an object – weight)

■ Measurement of variables

● length, thickness etc.

equipment

| micrometer (thickness of a hair) | callipers (diameter of a fruit) | tape (circumference of a tree) |

units
millimetre (mm), centimetre (10 mm), metre (1000 mm), micrometre (μm or simply μ) – a thousandth of a millimetre – used for microscopic measurements such as the length of a cell

● area

equipment
squared grid

units
square millimetres (mm²), square centimetres (100 mm²)

● volume

♦ solids   the volume of a solid can be found by calculation or by displacement of a liquid
units
cubic centimetres (cm³)

7

<table>
<tr><td>♦ liquids</td><td>**equipment**
measuring cylinder (for
liquids and powders)
units
millilitre (ml), litre (1000 ml)</td><td></td></tr>
</table>

♦ liquids   **equipment**
measuring cylinder (for
liquids and powders)
units
millilitre (ml), litre (1000 ml)

read
here

♦ gases   the volume of a gas is simply the volume of its
container

● **mass**   **equipment**
balance (compares with known masses,
usually called weights)
units
milligram (mg), gram (1000 mg), kilogram
(1000 000 mg)

● **force** (including **weight**)
             equipment
forcemeter (newtonmeter, spring balance)
units
newtons (N)

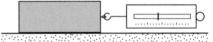

at the surface of the earth, a mass of 1 kg has
a weight of about 10 newtons

● **time**   **equipment**
stopwatch
units
second (s)

● **temperature** **equipment**
thermometer
units
degrees Celsius (°C)

8

■ Multiple unit measurements

● **density** $= \dfrac{\text{mass}}{\text{volume}}$

density is the mass of 1 cubic centimetre

$D = \dfrac{M}{V} \qquad V = \dfrac{M}{D} \qquad M = D \times V$

● **speed** $= \dfrac{\text{distance}}{\text{time}}$

speed is the distance travelled in 1 time unit

$S = \dfrac{D}{T} \qquad T = \dfrac{D}{S} \qquad D = S \times T$

● **pressure** $= \dfrac{\text{force}}{\text{area}}$

pressure is the force on 1 square centimetre

$P = \dfrac{F}{A} \qquad A = \dfrac{F}{P} \qquad F = P \times A$

1.2 DECISION MAKING

■ Investigations or experiments

In carrying out investigations or experiments, we need to make **decisions** about

● aims and objectives

● which variable to change in a **controlled** experiment,
  e.g. investigating the variables in the rusting of iron

9

- any necessary **safety** issues
  - ♦ be aware of possible hazards in the surroundings (including other people!)
  - ♦ be aware of possible personal hazards: long hair, jewellery, loose clothing, etc.
  - ♦ move carefully
  - ♦ take special care with chemicals and glass
  - ♦ wear protective clothing, e.g. goggles
  - ♦ assess the risks
  - ♦ know hazard symbols

 oxidising: the substances can provide oxygen which supports combustion, e.g. sodium chlorate, potassium nitrate, bleach

 highly flammable: the substances can readily catch fire, e.g. ethanol, methylated spirits, acetone, petrol

 toxic: the substances are poisonous and their effects could be fatal if they are swallowed, breathed in or absorbed through the skin, e.g. mercury and its compounds, copper sulphate

 harmful: the substances have the same effects as toxic substances but are less dangerous and unlikely to be fatal, e.g. dilute acids and alkalis

 corrosive: the substances attack and destroy living tissues; contact with the skin should be avoided and the eyes should be protected, e.g. concentrated acids and alkalis

 irritant: the substances are not corrosive but cause reddening or blistering of the skin, e.g. dilute acids and alkalis

In addition, we need to

- ask questions: what if?   why?   how?
- make observations
- take measurements using appropriate equipment and units
- record observations, measurements etc.
- display results using suitable tables, graphs etc.

■ Reasoning

From observations we can

- look for patterns
- make predictions
- draw conclusions taking into account the original aims and objectives
- make modifications to the aims and objectives for future investigation

1.3 TESTS AND TECHNIQUES

■ Tests

- for **acidic** and **alkaline** solutions – **pH indicators**

    ♦ **litmus** indicator is red in acid, blue in alkali

    ♦ **universal** or **full range** indicator has a range of colours for different pH values

- for **carbon dioxide**

    ♦ **limewater** (solution of calcium hydroxide) turns milky (cloudy) when carbon dioxide is bubbled through it

    ♦ **bicarbonate indicator** turns yellow

- for **starch: iodine** solution turns black (useful when looking at plant cells)

- for **water**
    - ♦ **anhydrous copper sulphate** turns blue
    - ♦ **cobalt chloride paper** turns pink
- for **oxygen:** glowing splint is reignited
- for **hydrogen:** makes a squeaky pop with a lighted splint
- for **carbonates:** add acid which reacts to form carbon dioxide (limewater test)

■ Techniques

- for making the **nucleus of a cell** more visible **methylene blue** (a dye) stains a cell nucleus purple

- for checking the purity of a **dye** (coloured substance) **chromatography** separates the different coloured components

1.4 REAL-LIFE SCIENCE

■ Life and living processes (biology)

healthy living (diet, exercise etc.), medicine, farming, conservation

■ Materials and their properties (chemistry)

burning, rusting, chemicals, pharmaceuticals, minerals, coal, oil

■ Physical processes (physics)

engineering, forces, machines, energy, electricity (hydro-electricity etc.), electronics, plumbing, weather, the seasons, astronomy

1.5 COMMON AREAS OF CONFUSION

■ **Mass and weight** *(see also pages 7–9)*

● the **mass** of an object is a measure of the amount of matter and this is the same wherever it is; 'old fashioned' weighing scales (balances) compare an unknown mass with known masses (commonly called weights!)

● the **weight** of an object is a measure of the gravitational force on it, which depends upon the mass of the object and its distance from the centre of Earth; many weighing scales which are forcemeters (newtonmeters), involving the extension of a spring, have scales marked in kilograms rather than newtons

● if someone says that his 'weight' is 70 kilograms, what he means is that he is pulled to the centre of Earth with the same gravitational force as a 70 kg mass, his mass is 70 kg and his weight is 700 N

■ **Force and pressure**

● **force** is a push or pull and may be applied to a point

● **pressure** is the result of applying a force spread over an area

■ **Excretion and egestion** *(see also page 18, 27, 29, 38)*

● **excretion** is the removal of cell waste from the blood, tissues and organs, e.g. urea and carbon dioxide

● **egestion** is the removal of solid waste from the digestive system as faeces

■ **Voltage and current**

● **voltage** is the 'push' which sends an electric current round a circuit

- **current** is the energy which does the work, gives the electric shock etc.

■ **Viruses and bacteria** *(see also pages 46, 47)*

- **viruses** are not living cells and are smaller than bacteria; they have 'life' only inside a host organism where they can make copies of themselves

- **bacteria** are living cells without nuclei

■ **Animals and mammals** *(see also page 39)*

- **animals** include all invertebrates and vertebrates

- **mammals** are just one group of vertebrate (backboned) animals

- we hear people talk about 'birds and animals' when they really mean 'birds and mammals'; birds *are* animals!

■ **Melting and dissolving**

- **melting** involves a change of state, from solid to liquid, of one substance

- **dissolving** involves the spreading out evenly of the molecules of one substance in another (usually a liquid)

■ **Breathing and respiration** *(see also page 30)*

- **breathing** is the gas exchange between an organism and the environment

- **respiration** is the process in which 'food' is converted into energy; it takes place in every living cell of every organism

- **artificial respiration** is assistance with breathing

- the **respiratory system** is the breathing system

■ Evaporating and boiling

● in **evaporating,** molecules of gas leave the surface of the liquid at all temperatures

● in **boiling,** bubbles of gas form throughout the liquid and these bubbles rise to the surface; a liquid has a particular temperature (its boiling point) at which all of the heat energy supplied goes into the change of state and the temperature does not rise

■ Salts and salt and salt

● **salts** are chemical compounds formed when metallic elements react with acids; there are numerous salts; **potassium nitrate, calcium carbonate, copper sulphate, zinc chloride** are all salts

● **salt** is an everyday name for just one salt, **sodium chloride**

● table **salt** is **sodium chloride** mixed with a little **potassium chloride**

■ Temperature and heat

● a **temperature** is a point on a temperature scale; it is a measurement of how hot or cold something is

● **heat** is a form of energy

● if you **heat** something (if heat energy is supplied) then the temperature will increase (unless a change of state is taking place, when it will stay the same)

● if you have a '**temperature**' this means that your body temperature is higher than the normal temperature of about 37 degrees Celsius

■ Radiation and radiators

- **radiation** is the transfer of energy from one place to another, other than by particles

- a central heating **radiator** warms a room by convection, not radiation!

■ Pollination and seed dispersal *(see also page 38)*

- **pollination** is the landing of pollen on the stigma of a flower, by the action of the wind, water, insects etc.

- **seed dispersal** is the dispersal (scattering) of seeds after fertilisation, by the action of the wind, water, animals or expulsion ('exploding' fruits)

2. BIOLOGY

2.1 LIFE PROCESSES

The seven life processes are: **m**ovement, **r**eproduction, **s**ensitivity, **g**rowth, **r**espiration, **e**xcretion, **n**utrition. (The mnemonic (memory aid) **MRS GREN** may be helpful.)

■ Similarities and differences between animals and green plants

Note: there are exceptions to most 'rules' in nature.

animals	green plants
movement can move freely	cannot move freely but some (usually slow) movement is made towards light and water
reproduction individual organisms usually either male or female; new individuals grow from fertilised eggs	individual organisms usually contain both male and female parts; new individuals grow from seeds
sensitivity respond quickly to the environment; respond to pain, danger etc.	grow in the direction opposite to the force of gravity; respond to light
growth individuals grow steadily throughout life, starting as a single cell and usually stop growing or grow more slowly in the final stages of life	
respiration releases the energy from food; this takes place in every living cell	

17

animals	green plants
excretion	
waste gases produced in respiration are put back into the atmosphere	
excess water and urea are removed in sweat and in urine	waste oxygen from photosynthesis is put back into the atmosphere
	excess materials are removed by shedding leaves
nutrition	
eat other animals or plants (dead or alive)	make food by photosynthesis from carbon dioxide (from the air) and water (from the soil)
water is essential to all living things	
some minerals are essential for health	

2.2 CELLS AND CELL FUNCTIONS

■ Cells

These are the simplest units of living matter which can maintain life and reproduce themselves.

● **parts of a cell**
  all cells have

  ♦ a **surface membrane** – surrounds the cell; substances can pass through

  ♦ **cytoplasm** – a gel-like material which makes up most of the cell; contains water and dissolved chemicals

  almost all cells have

  ♦ a **nucleus** – controls the activities of the cell; contains **genes** in the **DNA** which give the cell its characteristic

18

plant cells, in addition, have

♦ a **cell wall** made of cellulose which is fairly rigid and supports the cell; water and gases can pass through

plant cells, in addition, *usually* have

♦ a large, permanent, fluid-filled **vacuole** which stores chemicals

plant cells, in addition, *may* have within the cytoplasm

♦ **chloroplasts** containing **chlorophyll** which is needed to absorb the light energy used in **photosynthesis**

♦ **starch granules** (food stores)

● **sizes of cells**

♦ about 50 typical **animal cells** could be placed on a pinhead

♦ about 10 typical **plant cells** could be placed on a pinhead

● **typical animal and plant cells**

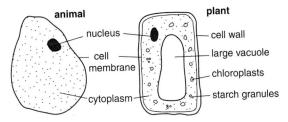

● **specialised animal cells**

Note: the drawings are not to the same scale.

♦ **epithelial cells** are packed tightly together and form 'barriers' which protect parts of the body

19

♦ **nerve cells** are long and thin and carry electrical impulses

♦ **muscle cells** can contract and then relax again

♦ **white blood cells** defend the body against infection by trapping and destroying microbes

♦ **red blood cells** (do not have a nucleus) contain haemoglobin which can combine with oxygen; carry oxygen to all parts of the body; are made in some bones; wear out after about 20 weeks

♦ **sperm cells** (male sex cells)

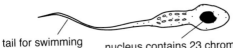

tail for swimming   nucleus contains 23 chromosomes
(half of genetic information)

♦ **egg cells** (female sex cells)

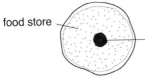

food store   nucleus contains
23 chromosomes
(half of genetic
information)

sex cells are also known as gametes

● **specialised plant cells**

♦ **root hair cell**

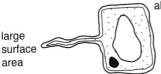

absorbs water from soil

large
surface
area

● **single-celled organisms**

some organisms consist of a single, very specialised, cell
e.g. *Amoeba, Paramecium, Euglena*

■ Cell division

- cells multiply by dividing! – the process involves division of both the nucleus and the cytoplasm

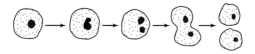

- new cells are formed all the time by the division of old cells

- new cells are necessary for
  - ♦ growth
  - ♦ replacement
  - ♦ repair

- new cells are made only as they are needed, but occasionally the cell division may get out of control (because of a problem with the genes, or because of environmental factors such as smoking) and a cancer may develop

■ Cells and the human body

- the human body, which is made up of an estimated 100 thousand million cells, starts as a single newly-fertilised egg cell (zygote)

- a **tissue** is a group of similar cells which perform a special function

- an **organ** consists of at least two types of tissue organised so that they work together for a common purpose

- a **system** is an organised group of organs arranged so that they perform the complex functions of the body

■ Tissues

There are 4 main types of tissue in the human body

- **epithelial tissue** where the cells are packed tightly together to form continuous sheets which form the linings of organs and help to protect them, e.g. the outer layer of skin, the inside of the mouth, the inside of the stomach

- **connective tissues** of many types add support and structure to the body

  ♦ inner layers of skin

  ♦ tendons

  ♦ ligaments

  ♦ cartilage

  ♦ bone

  ♦ fat

  ♦ blood (considered to be a form of connective tissue – *see under 'organs'*)

- **muscle tissue** is specialised tissue which can contract and relax

- **nerve tissue** can generate and conduct electrical impulses in the body; nerve tissue in the brain manages the impulses and transmits them down the spinal cord to all parts of the body

■ Organs

- **brain** – the most complex organ, which affects and governs

  ♦ all the nervous impulses in the body

  ♦ what you think and do; how you feel; what kind of person you are

- **blood** – one tiny drop contains millions of blood cells and other parts

    ♦ red cells – transport oxygen

    ♦ white cells – fight infection

    ♦ platelets – help with clotting

    ♦ plasma – the fluid

- **eyes** – most highly developed of the **sense** organs

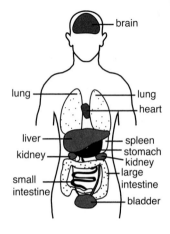

- **heart** – a pump which circulates blood

    ♦ never rests throughout life

    ♦ is extremely efficient

    ♦ its moving parts are almost indestructible

- **intestines**

    ♦ **small intestine** where digested foods are absorbed

    ♦ **large intestine** where water is absorbed

- **kidneys** – act as a filter

    ♦ monitor quality of blood

    ♦ separate harmful substances from useful ones

    ♦ act as waste disposal units

- **liver** – the 'distribution centre'
    - ◆ largest and heaviest internal organ
    - ◆ in upper part of abdomen; partly protected by rib cage
    - ◆ sorts out dissolved food molecules and sends them to where they are needed
    - ◆ breaks down toxins
- **lungs** – the gas exchange centre
- **pancreas** – the gland in the abdomen
    - ◆ produces enzymes
    - ◆ produces hormones
- **skin** – the largest and heaviest organ of the body
- **stomach** – juices digest protein, stomach acids kill bacteria ingested with food

■ Systems

There are ten systems in the human body, each consisting of two or more organs.

- **skeletal system** (bones, cartilage, tendons, ligaments)
    - ◆ provides support for the body
    - ◆ protects delicate organs
    - ◆ provides attachment sites for the muscles

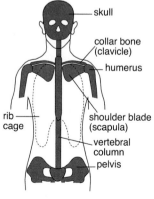

skull

collar bone (clavicle)

humerus

rib cage

shoulder blade (scapula)

vertebral column

pelvis

- **muscular system** (muscles)
  - ◆ work in pairs to move limbs
  - ◆ control movement of materials through some organs such as the stomach and intestines
  - ◆ operate the heart and the circulatory system
- **circulatory system** (heart, blood vessels)
  transports blood through the body for carrying
  - ◆ nutrients
  - ◆ gases – oxygen and carbon dioxide
  - ◆ hormones
  - ◆ wastes
- **nervous system** (brain, spinal cord, peripheral nerves)
  - ◆ relays electrical messages through the body
  - ◆ directs behaviour and movement
  - ◆ helps with control of digestion, circulation etc.
- **breathing system** (nose, trachea [windpipe], lungs)
  - ◆ provides gas exchange surface between the blood and the external environment
  - ◆ oxygen is absorbed
  - ◆ carbon dioxide is exhaled
- **digestive system** (mouth, oesophagus, stomach, small and large intestines)
  - ◆ breaks down and absorbs nutrients necessary for growth and maintenance

- **excretory system** (kidneys, ureters, bladder, urethra)
  filters from the circulatory system

  ♦ dissolved wastes

  ♦ excess water

  ♦ excess nutrients

- **endocrine system** (various glands)
  relays chemical messages through the body

  ♦ glands secrete hormones

  ♦ helps with control of nutrient absorption, growth etc.

- **reproductive system** (**female**: ovaries, oviducts, uterus,
  vagina); (**male**: testes, penis)

- **immune (lymphatic) system**
  lymph (white blood cells) protects the body

  ♦ destroys and removes invading bacteria and viruses

  ♦ removes fat and excess fluids from the blood

2.3 HUMANS AND OTHER ANIMALS

■ **Nutrition**

- **teeth:** a feature only of **vertebrate** (backboned) animals –
  mammals, reptiles and fishes (but not birds or amphibians)

  ♦ teeth of mammals are of four main types:
    – incisors (cutting, chopping);
    – canines (tearing, killing);
    – pre-molars (grinding, tearing);
    – molars (grinding, crushing)

♦ tooth **decay** is caused by acid which is formed by bacteria from sugar left on the teeth; the acid attacks the enamel coating

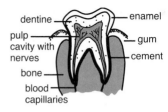

dentine — enamel
pulp cavity with nerves — gum
— cement
bone
blood capillaries

● **food** is necessary to provide materials for

♦ growth – proteins

♦ energy for activity – carbohydrates (starches and sugars), fats

♦ helping growth and energy to be effective – minerals, vitamins, fibre, water

♦ insulation – fats

● a balanced **diet** contains the right proportions of

♦ **protein** meat, chicken, fish, eggs, baked beans

♦ **carbohydrates** starches (broken down slowly) bread, cereals, potatoes, pasta
sugars (broken down quickly) sweets, fizzy drinks

♦ **fats** (can be stored in layers beneath the skin) cheese, butter, milk, meat

♦ **minerals** (needed in building teeth, bones, red blood cells) meat, milk, vegetables

♦ **vitamins** (in very small quantities) fruit, vegetables, milk, butter, cheese

♦ **water** (for man, at least 1.5 litres a day) drinks, fruit, vegetables

♦ **fibre** (mostly plant cell walls; helps egestion of solid waste) cereals, fruit, vegetables

● **digestion** takes place in the **alimentary canal** (gut)

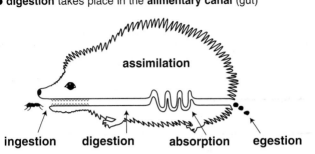

ingestion **digestion** **absorption** **egestion**

♦ **digestion: physical** by chewing and action of muscles;
  chemical by **enzymes** in the mouth, stomach and small
  intestine

♦ **absorption:** soluble food molecules pass into the
  bloodstream through villi in the wall of the small intestine;
  water is absorbed in large intestine

♦ **assimilation:** soluble food molecules are carried to all
  parts of the body to be used for growth, energy and
  maintenance

♦ **egestion:** solid waste is stored as **faeces** in the rectum,
  and egested

● **enzymes**

♦ come in a variety of types, adapted to dealing with
  different foods

♦ considerably speed up the breakdown of food

♦ are re-useable since they are not affected by the process

- **circulation** transports food and oxygen to all living cells in the body

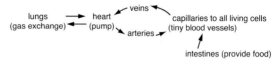

- **breathing:** air entering and leaving the lungs due to the action of the rib muscles and diaphragm

- **gas exchange** takes place in the **air sacs** in the lungs

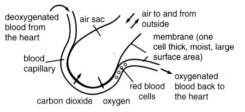

■ **Respiration**

This takes place in every living cell of all organisms.

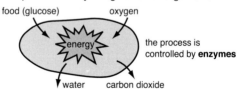

- **respiration** is a chemical change (reaction) and can be represented by the **word equation**

$$\text{glucose} + \text{oxygen} \xrightarrow[\text{RELEASED}]{\text{ENERGY}} \text{carbon dioxide} + \text{water}$$

- the **energy** produced in respiration is necessary for all life processes but particularly for

    ♦ growing

    ♦ maintaining a constant body temperature

    ♦ moving (by muscle contraction)

- **exercise**

    ♦ increases strength by increasing muscle strength

    ♦ builds up stamina by making the lungs and heart more efficient

    ♦ uses energy which lowers the risk of obesity

Movement

Vertebrate animals move by using muscles to move bones.

- the **skeleton**

    ♦ consists of **bones** connected by **ligaments** which can stretch

    ♦ provides **protection** for vital organs (e.g. the skull protects the brain)

    ♦ provides **support** for the body

    ♦ is the source of red blood cells (made in the bone marrow of some bones)

    ♦ stores minerals

- **muscles**

    ♦ are attached to bones by **tendons** which cannot stretch

    ♦ usually work across moveable joints in **antagonistic** pairs

    ♦ contract to pull on the bones

- **joints** allow movement

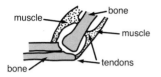 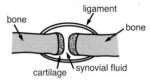

  - ♦ **cartilage** and **synovial fluid** ensure that a joint works
    smoothly (absorbs shock)

  - ♦ the elbow is an example of a **hinge joint**

  - ♦ the shoulder is an example of a **ball and socket joint**

■ Growth and the life cycle

- **a lifetime**

fertilisation	conception	birth	childhood	puberty	death
ovum (egg) and sperm (gametes)	fertilised egg cell (zygote)	embryo fetus	baby toddler child	adolescent	adult elderly person
		gestation period	rapid growth development of brain	big changes especially in reproductive organs	growth stops life processes stop

- **changes in adolescence**
  at **puberty** the big changes, both internal and external, are
  controlled by **sex hormones** (male testosterone; female
  oestrogen and progesterone)

  - ♦ in both sexes: period of rapid growth; pubic hair grows

♦ in males: voice deepens; testes and penis develop; muscles develop

♦ in females: hips widen; breasts develop; periods start (menstruation)

in addition, individuals gain greater independence from parents and become more responsible for actions

■ Reproduction (the process of producing offspring)

● **gametes** (sex cells)

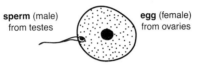

sperm (male)
from testes

egg (female)
from ovaries

● **making a new individual**

♦ in **fertilisation**, the nucleus of one sperm (of the hundreds of millions released) enters an egg as it travels down the **fallopian tube** (oviduct); the two nuclei fuse

♦ the **zygote** (fertilised egg) divides to become a ball of cells as it travels towards the **uterus** (womb)

♦ in **implantation**, a ball of cells becomes successfully embedded in the thickened wall of the uterus

♦ a **placenta** develops at this point and an **embryo** develops, attached to the placenta by an **umbilical cord**

♦ the embryo develops within an **amniotic sac** filled with **amniotic fluid** which protects the embryo

♦ once the embryo develops human characteristics, it is called a **fetus**

- through the placenta, the embryo receives all it needs (soluble food and oxygen) and gets rid of waste (carbon dioxide and urea)

- the uterus provides constant temperature, protection from infection and protection from physical shock

■ Health

- **diet** is very important and malnutrition can result from

  - lack of vitamin C, calcium and other minerals, leading to deficiency diseases

  - excess of animal fats, leading to obesity

- **smoking** can harm the lungs and respiratory passages because the smoke

  - lacks moisture

  - is hot

  - contains harmful chemicals including:

    - **nicotine** which is addictive and also alters the heart rate

    - **tar** which can cause lung cancer

    - **carbon monoxide** which replaces oxygen in red blood cells and affects transport of oxygen round the body

  - reduces the surface area of the lungs, leading to breathing difficulties

- **drugs** are substances which change the normal activities of the body

  - some drugs are beneficial if used sensibly, e.g. paracetamol

  - many drugs are addictive and can present serious health risks

- **diseases** may be caused by
  - ◆ bacteria *(see page 46)*
  - ◆ viruses *(see page 47)*
  - ◆ fungi *(see page 40)*
- the body has **natural defences**
  - ◆ skin
  - ◆ reactions to pain etc.
  - ◆ immunisation helps to build up the body's natural defences

2.4 GREEN PLANTS

■ Movement

- unlike most animals, green plants do not move from place to place but grow attached to soil by roots; some (usually slow) movement towards light is normal and the roots grow towards water

■ Nutrition

- green plants make their own food (biomass) in the process of **photosynthesis**, which takes place in the leaves and stems, using chlorophyll in the chloroplasts of the cells
- the **food** made is stored as starch
  - ◆ in the leaves
  - ◆ underground in storage organs

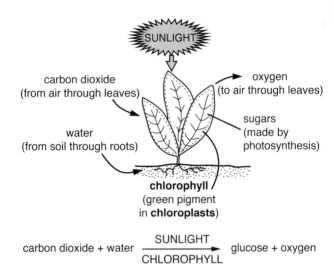

$$\text{carbon dioxide} + \text{water} \xrightarrow[\text{CHLOROPHYLL}]{\text{SUNLIGHT}} \text{glucose} + \text{oxygen}$$

- **minerals** are necessary for the development of healthy leaves, roots and fruits

  - ♦ **nitrates** for making proteins

  - ♦ **phosphates** for healthy, widespread roots

  - ♦ **magnesium** compounds for the production of chlorophyll

  - ♦ **potassium** compounds for maintaining cell size, thereby helping in photosynthesis

  a fertiliser usually contains the appropriate mixture of minerals

- **roots**

  - ♦ anchor the plant to the ground

  - ♦ take in water from the soil

  - ♦ take in minerals from the soil

■ Growth and the life cycle

● a lifetime

fertilisation		dispersal	germination	maturity	death
male sex cell (in pollen) female sex cell (in ovule) (gametes)	fertilised egg cell (zygote) embryo (seed inside fruit)	seed moved to new location by wind, water, animals etc.	new individual develops from seed using stored food	plant makes food by photo- synthesis and grows	life processes stop

■ Respiration

(see page 30)

■ Reproduction

This can be by various means but typically, flowering plants reproduce sexually.

● flowers

♦ **sepals** protect a flower whilst it is a bud

♦ **stamens** provide male sex cells: filament, anther

♦ **carpels** provide female sex cells: ovary, ovule, stigma, style

♦ **petals** are often bright and have an attractive smell

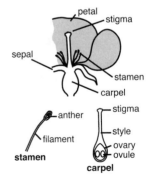

37

- ♦ **nectaries** of the carpel produce nectar (sugar solution) which attracts insects

- in **pollination**, pollen from an **anther** (male part) is carried to the **stigma** (female part)

  it is best if the pollen is carried to the stigma of a different flower by an insect or the wind etc.

- following **fertilisation** of an egg cell, the cell divides to become an **embryo**

- a **seed** consists of an embryo and a food **store** (**cotyledons** – sometimes known as seed 'leaves')

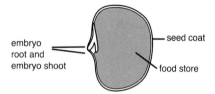

embryo root and embryo shoot — seed coat — food store

- a **fruit** (what is left of the ovary) may contain one seed or many seeds

- in **dispersal**, seeds are carried to a new location by wind, water, animals or by 'exploding' fruits

- for **germination**, a seed (embryo and food store) needs water, oxygen and a suitably warm temperature (The mnemonic 'WOW' may be helpful.)

- ■ **Excretion**

  - ♦ excess oxygen is released to the air from the leaves

  - ♦ leaves are shed, either a few at a time all the year round (evergreen plants) or all at once in the autumn (deciduous plants)

2.5 FUNGI AND BACTERIA

Fungi and bacteria are important in the process of **decomposition**: the breaking down of dead animals and plants and excreted animal waste, releasing raw materials back into the environment.

● **carbon dioxide** is released from the breakdown of carbohydrates, fats and proteins

● **nitrates** are released from proteins (very useful for plant nutrition)

Fungi cannot photosynthesise (they are not green).

2.6 VARIATION AND CLASSIFICATION

Note: there are exceptions to most general statements.

■ Classification

The classification of organisms (living things) into groups helps in understanding the process of **evolution**.

● **animals**

♦ **vertebrates**
   fishes, amphibians, reptiles, birds, mammals

	fishes	amphibians	reptiles	birds	mammals
warm blooded				✔	✔
feed young on milk					✔
lay eggs — in water	✔	✔			
lay eggs — on land			✔	✔	
skin has scales	✔		✔		
skin has feathers				✔	
skin has fur					✔

♦ **invertebrates**
    arthropods (insects, spiders, woodlice, crabs etc.)
    echinoderms (starfishes, sea urchins etc.)
    molluscs (snails, slugs, bivalves, squids etc.)
    annelids (earthworms, leeches etc.)
    and many other groups

● **green plants**

  ♦ **flowering plants**
    some have seeds exposed in cones; most have seeds
    protected in fruits; some are evergreen; some are
    deciduous

  ♦ **non-flowering plants**
    ferns, mosses, liverworts etc.

● **algae** are simple organisms which make food by
  photosynthesis

● **lichens** consist of an alga (which provides the food) and a
  fungus (which provides the support)

● **fungi**

  ♦ **parasites** feed on living organisms

  ♦ **saprophytes** feed on dead organisms and animal waste

● **microbes** (micro-organisms) are too small to be seen with
  the unaided eye

  ♦ those with a nucleus (e.g. protozoa such as *Amoeba*,
    Paramecium)

  ♦ those without a nucleus (**bacteria**) *(see page 46)*

  ♦ those which have 'life' only inside a host organism
    (**viruses**) *(see page 47)*

■ Small classification groups

● organisms of the same **species** can interbreed to produce fertile offspring

● each species has a two-word Latin name; **genus** (first word) then species, e.g. *Homo sapiens*

● related species are in the same genus (have the same **generic** name), e.g. *Homo neanderthalis* is an extinct species related to modern man

■ Variation

● there are differences (sometimes only very slight) between individuals of the same species; variations depend upon:

♦ **genetic makeup** inherited from male and female parents in fertilisation (inherited variation)

♦ **environmental factors:** food supply, sunlight, atmospheric pollution, temperature, (environmental variation)

■ Inheritance

● half sets of genes are carried by chromosomes in the nuclei of the gametes

2.7 LIVING THINGS IN THEIR ENVIRONMENT

■ Environment

The environment in which an organism lives, consists of everything in its surroundings.

● air, water, rocks and soil

● community: animal life, plant life, microbes

within an environment there may be many different **habitats**, e.g. seashore (environment); rock pool (habitat)

■ Habitat

The habitat of an organism

- is the part of the environment in which it lives
- provides it with
  - ◆ food (or in the case of green plants the materials to make food)
  - ◆ shelter from danger and hazardous weather conditions
  - ◆ a suitable and safe place to breed
- may change because of
  - ◆ natural events, e.g. torrential rain, tide movements
  - ◆ man-made events, e.g. an oil spill, deforestation (cutting down forests)

■ Niche

The niche of an organism is the **role** it plays in the ecosystem.

■ Human impact

Human impact on the environment is considerable and increasing.

- changes to the atmosphere
  - ◆ destruction of the ozone layer (which filters out harmful UV rays of sunlight) by CFCs
  - ◆ increased levels of carbon dioxide produced in burning fossil fuels, and contributing to the greenhouse effect (global warming)

- increased levels of carbon dioxide because of the destruction of forests which would remove carbon dioxide in photosynthesis

- gases such as nitrous oxide and sulphur dioxide dissolve in water in the atmosphere to fall as 'acid rain'

- pollution of rivers and the sea

- upsetting the balance of nature by

  - deliberately, carelessly or accidentally killing organisms, e.g. trapping birds of prey

  - destroying or drastically changing a habitat, e.g. cutting down a forest

  - using chemicals or pesticides

  - introducing species to an existing environment, e.g. rabbits in Australia, growing GM (genetically modified) crops

■ Conservation

This involves protection of the environment by

- maintaining a balance between the activities of man and the natural world, e.g. sustainable development

- preservation of habitats

- creating habitats, e.g. 'wild areas' in gardens and providing nest boxes etc.

- protection of endangered species

■ Adaptation and competition

- an **adaptation** is a feature which helps an organism to survive in its environment; it may help an organism to

  - hunt, e.g. powerful muscles, good eyesight

♦ hide, e.g. camouflage

♦ cope with extremes of temperature, e.g. blubber

♦ cope with seasonal changes, e.g. hibernation, migration, losing leaves

♦ catch a particular prey species, e.g. nocturnal

● competition between species, or between individuals of the same species, results in the 'survival of the fittest'

■ Food chains and feeding relationships

● a **food chain** shows the energy flow from organism to organism

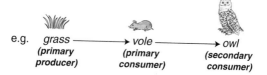

e.g. *grass* ⟶ *vole* ⟶ *owl*
(primary producer)   (primary consumer)   (secondary consumer)

● a **producer** makes food by photosynthesis

● a **consumer** may be

♦ a **herbivore** – eats plants

♦ a **carnivore** – eats animals

♦ an **omnivore** – eats a mixture of plants and animals

● a **predator** is an animal which catches and eats other animals; the animals caught are the **prey**

● a **parasite** takes nourishment from a living organism, usually without harming it in any major way

♦ parasitic animals, e.g. tick (external parasite), tapeworm (internal parasite)

- ♦ parasitic plants, e.g. mistletoe
- a **saprophyte** takes nourishment from dead organisms
  - ♦ many fungi are saprophytic
- **predator-prey relationship**
  - ♦ decreasing the number of a predator species will increase the number of a prey species
  - ♦ there is ideally a balance between the numbers of predators and prey
  - ♦ there is a cycle in the numbers of predators and their prey
- a **food web**
  - ♦ shows feeding relationships in a habitat
  - ♦ consists of interlinked food chains

e.g.

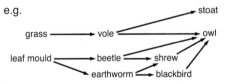

  - ♦ can be seriously affected by changes in the circumstances of any organism, e.g. use of pesticides to kill beetles
- a **food 'pyramid'** (often not like a pyramid!) takes account of the numbers of organisms at each level of a food chain

■ Population

A population is

- the number of organisms of a species living, at the same time, in one habitat

- subject to change because of

  - ♦ births

  - ♦ deaths due to natural causes, being eaten, or disease

  - ♦ individuals joining, e.g. attraction of plentiful food supply

  - ♦ individuals leaving, e.g. food is in short supply, or there is overcrowding

■ Microorganisms

These play an important part in the environment.

● bacteria

- ♦ are tiny microbes, smaller than typical cells but larger than viruses

- ♦ have a cell wall, membrane, cytoplasm and genes, but no nucleus

- ♦ reproduce by splitting – very rapidly!

- ♦ live inside an organism, or on the outside surface

- ♦ make use of the host organism's food

- ♦ release toxins (poisonous substances) which can harm the host

- ♦ are responsible for many human diseases, e.g. TB, tetanus, tooth decay

- ♦ can be controlled by antibiotics (inside the body), antiseptics (on the outside surface of the body), disinfectants (on non-living surfaces)
- ♦ play a vital role in the decomposition of dead bodies and animal waste

- **viruses**
  - ♦ are very tiny microbes
  - ♦ have 'life' only when they enter a living organism
  - ♦ consist of a few genes inside a protein coat
  - ♦ can make copies of themselves inside the host cells
  - ♦ are responsible for many human diseases, e.g. 'flu, mumps, measles
  - ♦ cannot be controlled by antibiotics
  - ♦ may be controlled by vaccination

3. CHEMISTRY

3.1 GROUPING AND CLASSIFYING MATERIALS

■ Physical properties of materials

materials which are

- **hard** are not easily scratched and do not easily change shape, e.g. diamond

- **strong** are not easily broken, e.g. steel girder

- **rigid** do not bend easily, e.g. steel girder

- **flexible** bend easily, e.g. fibreglass fishing rod

- **elastic** stretch easily, e.g. rubber band

- **compressible** can be squeezed into a smaller space, e.g. sponge

  (Materials which are flexible, elastic or compressible usually return to the original form when the forces are removed.)

- **dense** appear to be 'heavy' compared to similar sized pieces of other materials, e.g. lead

some materials

- **expand** when they are heated, e.g. steel railway lines

- **change state** when they are heated or cooled

materials which are

- **thermal conductors** readily conduct heat energy, e.g. aluminium saucepan

- **thermal insulators** do not conduct heat energy, e.g. plastic handle on saucepan

- **electrical conductors** readily conduct electricity, e.g. copper cable

- **electrical insulators** do not conduct electricity,
  e.g. plastic covering of copper cable

- **magnetic** are attracted to a magnet, e.g. iron

materials which are:

- **transparent** allow light to pass through, e.g. window glass

- **translucent** allow some light to pass through,
  e.g. plastic milk bottle

- **opaque** do not allow light to pass through, e.g. copper coin

- **shiny** reflect light easily, e.g. polished silver

- **dull** do not reflect light easily, but if you can see them they
  do reflect light!

- **white** reflect a wide spectrum of colours

- **black** reflect all colours equally badly

- **red** reflect red light best

materials which are:

- **absorbent** readily soak up water, e.g. sponge

- **porous** allow water to pass through, e.g. filter paper

- **permeable** allow water to soak through, e.g. some rocks

- **waterproof** do not allow water to pass through, e.g.
  Gore-tex raincoat

■ **Naturally occurring materials**

- **rocks** are of three main types

  ♦ **igneous rocks** – formed by the cooling of molten material
    slow cooling (deep in the earth) gives larger 'grains' of
    components, e.g. granite

fast cooling (e.g. on surface of the earth) gives smaller 'grains', e.g. basalt

♦ **sedimentary rocks** – formed by the settling of small particles of other rocks (on land or, much more commonly, in water), e.g. sandstone, shale
sedimentary rocks often contain **fossils**

♦ **metamorphic rocks** – formed from other rocks by the action of extreme heat and/or pressure, e.g. gneiss, slate

● rocks are composed of **minerals**

♦ some minerals are almost pure chemical elements or compounds

♦ many minerals are impure (mixtures)

♦ an **ore** is a naturally-occurring rock or mineral from which a metal may be extracted

● **soils** are formed from weathered (worn down) rocks and **humus** (the remains of organic materials)

■ The particle theory

This helps us to understand how materials are formed and the way in which they behave.

● a pure material is known as a **substance**

● **atoms** are the simplest particles which can make up an element – there are about 100 types of atom

● most substances are made up of **molecules**

● a **molecule** is made up of two or more atoms (of the same type or of differing types) chemically bonded together

■ States of matter

(In the drawings below the circles represent molecules or atoms.)

● **solid**

  ♦ the particles are held close together by forces and simply vibrate about fixed positions

  ♦ a solid usually retains its shape

  ♦ a solid cannot be compressed

● **liquid**

  ♦ the particles are held close together by forces but move freely around each other

  ♦ a liquid flows and takes the shape of its container

  ♦ a liquid cannot be compressed

● **gas**

  ♦ the particles are relatively far apart and move freely but bump into each other

  ♦ a gas fills any space which is available to it

  ♦ a gas can be compressed

  ♦ a gas has mass which can be measured

● **changes of state**

  ♦ some substances change state when they are heated or cooled

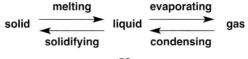

♦ some solids have a **melting point** (a temperature) at which all the heat energy supplied is used to break the close ties which hold the particles in fixed positions (in the case of ice this is more commonly known as the **freezing point** of water, 0 °C)

♦ some liquids have a **boiling point** at which all the heat energy supplied is used for the particles to break free from the others (in the case of water this occurs, under normal circumstances, at 100 °C)

♦ **evaporation** and **condensation** occur over a wide **temperature** range

● some useful **temperatures**

⁻273 °C	⁻39 °C	0 °C
absolute zero	mercury melts	water (ice) melts
37 °C	100 °C	1063 °C
normal human	water boils	gold melts
	6000 °C	
	surface of Sun	

Note: absolute zero is the calculated minimum possible temperature; it may be unattainable!

■ Elements and compounds

● an **element**

♦ is a simple substance, e.g. copper (solid), mercury (liquid), oxygen (gas)

♦ consists of atoms or of molecules which contain only one type of atom (there are only about 100 elements)

♦ has a unique place in the **periodic table** which shows the elements with similar properties in columns

- a **compound**
  - ♦ is a pure substance which consists of two or more elements chemically **combined** together, e.g. sodium chloride (solid), water (liquid), carbon dioxide (gas)
  - ♦ consists of molecules which contain two or more types of atom linked in a fixed ratio
- each element and compound has its own **formula** which shows the number of each type of atom in its molecule
  - ♦ elements, e.g. Cu (copper), Hg (mercury), O_2 (oxygen)
  - ♦ compounds, e.g. NaCl (sodium chloride), H_2O (water), CO_2 (carbon dioxide)

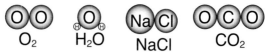

$$O_2 \qquad H_2O \qquad NaCl \qquad CO_2$$

(In these drawings the circles represent atoms.)

- **Mixtures**

A mixture consists of two or more types of molecule.

- some mixtures are the same all the way through
  - ♦ an **alloy** is a mixture of metals, e.g. brass, bronze, steel
  - ♦ a **solution** is a mixture of a solid, liquid or gas and a liquid
- some mixtures are not the same all the way through, e.g. soils, concrete, soup, most rocks
- **air** is a mixture of nitrogen (almost 80%), oxygen (about 20%), carbon dioxide etc.

3.2 CHANGING MATERIALS

Note: there are exceptions to most rules!

■ Physical changes

As a general rule, these

● are **reversible** if the conditions are reversed

● alter the appearance (i.e. state) of the material

● do not involve the formation of new substances

Heating and **cooling** substances can result in physical changes.

♦ **expansion**, e.g. steel railway tracks (solid), mercury in a thermometer (liquid), hot air balloon (gas), water (when it freezes)

♦ **change of state** *(see pages 14, 52)*

♦ a few solid substances **sublime** (change state from solid to gas without going through the liquid state) when heated

● **dissolving** one substance in another is a type of mixing in which every part of the resulting **solution** has the same composition as every other part

♦ solid common salt (a **solute**) dissolves in water (a **solvent**) to form salt solution
the process can be reversed by evaporating the water to leave the salt and condensing the water vapour

♦ whisky dissolves in water when it is diluted;
the process can be reversed by distilling the mixture to remove the alcohol which can then be condensed

♦ the gas carbon dioxide dissolves in water under pressure when fizzy drinks are made;
the process can be reversed by releasing the pressure

- ♦ the **solubility** of a solid in water increases with increasing temperature
  the solubility of a gas in water decreases with increasing temperature

- ♦ some substances which do not dissolve in water may dissolve in another solvent such as ethanol or propanone

- other physical changes include

  - ♦ **magnetising:** iron, cobalt, nickel and steel

  - ♦ **charging electrostatically:** amber, animal fur, some plastics and other man-made materials

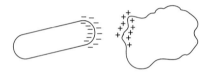

- the **water cycle** is a series of physical changes in nature

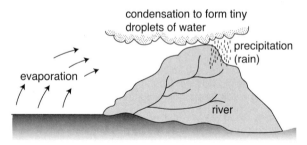

■ Chemical changes

As a general rule, these

- are **irreversible** (permanent)

- involve the formation of **new substances**
- can be represented by **word equations** such as

  ◆ combination (burning)
    hydrogen + oxygen $\longrightarrow$ water

  ◆ decomposition (action of yeast)
    sugar $\longrightarrow$ ethanol + carbon dioxide

- chemical changes in **nature** include

  ◆ **respiration** in every cell of all living things

    sugar + oxygen $\xrightarrow[\text{RELEASED}]{\text{ENERGY}}$ carbon dioxide + water

  ◆ **photosynthesis** in green plants

    carbon dioxide + water $\xrightarrow{\text{LIGHT ENERGY}}$ sugar + oxygen

- chemical changes associated with the **activities of man** include

  ◆ **burning** wood (in forest fires)

    wood + oxygen $\longrightarrow$ carbon dioxide + water + ash

  ◆ **rusting** iron

    iron + oxygen $\xrightarrow{\text{in presence of water}}$ iron oxide

■ **Geological changes**

These include

- the formation of rocks *(see pages 50–51)*

- **weathering** of rocks by the action of

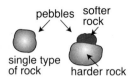

pebbles   softer rock

single type of rock

harder rock

  - ♦ wind
  - ♦ water movement of rain, rivers or the sea
  - ♦ freezing water (the expansion forces cracks to widen etc.)
- movement of molten material from deep in the earth resulting in volcanic eruptions
- movement at the surface of the earth resulting in earthquakes
- movement on the sea bed resulting in tsunamis

3.3 SEPARATING MIXTURES

■ Sieving

This is useful for separating solid particles from other solid particles or a liquid.

- sieving with holes you can see
  - ♦ garden sieve – separating small stones from soil
  - ♦ colander – separating rice from water
  - ♦ tea strainer – separating tea leaves from tea
- **filtering** is sieving with holes you cannot see
  - ♦ coffee filter
  - ♦ filter funnel and filter paper used in the laboratory
  - ♦ the solid material which does not pass through the filter is the **residue**
  the liquid which has passed through is the **filtrate**

■ Settling

This makes use of the fact that dense substances sink.

● sand in sea water settles and the water can be **decanted** (poured off)

● in gold panning, the gold particles settle and less dense particles are washed away

■ Flotation

This makes use of the fact that some substances float in water but others do not.

■ Evaporation of water

This leaves a dissolved solid – used in the extraction of salt from sea water.

■ Distillation

This can be used to separate a mixture of liquids – used in distilleries.

■ Chromatography

This can be used to separate dissolved solids – used to separate the dyes in ink.

3.4 PATTERNS OF BEHAVIOUR

Note: there are exceptions to almost all rules!

■ Metallic elements

● more than 80 elements are metallic or semi-metallic

● metals are solids at normal temperatures (except mercury which is always liquid)

- in general, metals
  - are strong
  - are shiny (reflect light)
  - are malleable (can be moulded or beaten into different shapes)
  - conduct heat
  - conduct electricity
  - are dense
  - have high melting points
- some metals
  - are magnetic (iron, cobalt, nickel and their alloys)
  - corrode (react with air and/or water to form oxides and other compounds)
  - are found in the natural state as the element (e.g. gold) but most are found only in compounds
  - are more reactive than others; metals can be ordered in a **reactivity series** by comparing the way they react with oxygen, water etc.

most reactive	potassium	difficult to extract from
	aluminium	their compounds
	zinc	
	iron	known since ancient
	tin	times; bronze is an alloy
	lead	of copper and tin
	copper	found in the natural state
	silver	as the element; used for
least reactive	gold	coins since ancient times

- **alloys** are mixtures of metallic elements and have a combination of the properties of those elements, e.g. strength and low density (lightness)

■ Non-metallic elements

- about 20 elements are non-metals
  - ♦ bromine is the only non-metal which is a liquid at normal temperatures; the others are solids, e.g. sulphur, carbon, or gases, e.g. oxygen, nitrogen
- in general, non-metals
  - ♦ are not strong
  - ♦ are not shiny
  - ♦ cannot be moulded or beaten into different shapes
  - ♦ are not good conductors of heat
  - ♦ are not good conductors of electricity
  - ♦ are not dense
  - ♦ have low melting points
- some non-metals
  - ♦ may be found in the natural state as the element, e.g. oxygen, carbon (as diamond) but most are found only in compounds
  - ♦ are found **only** as the element and do not form compounds, e.g. argon, neon
- some major exceptions are
  - ♦ diamond (a form of carbon) is the hardest known substance
  - ♦ graphite (a form of carbon) conducts electricity

■ Compounds

● compounds consist of two or more elements chemically combined

● compounds containing metallic elements are solids at normal temperatures, e.g. copper oxide

● compounds containing non-metals only, may be solids, e.g. polythene, liquids, e.g. water, or gases, e.g. carbon dioxide

● **oxides of metals**

   ♦ are formed when a metal combines with oxygen

   ♦ are **basic** and may dissolve in water to form **alkaline** solutions

● **oxides of non-metals**

   ♦ are formed when a non-metal combines with oxygen

   ♦ are **acidic** and may dissolve in water to form **acidic** solutions

● a **salt** is formed when a metal reacts with an acid

   e.g.   iron + sulphuric acid ⟶ iron sulphate + hydrogen
   (a salt)

● an **indicator** changes colour in acidic and/or alkaline solution

   ♦ **litmus** is red in acidic solution, blue in alkaline solution

   ♦ **universal** (or full range) indicator goes through a wide range of colours depending upon the **pH value** of the solution

pH1	pH7	pH14
strong acid	weak acid neutral weak alkali	strong alkali

♦ an acidic solution can be **neutralised** by adding an appropriate quantity of an alkaline solution

■ Chemical reactions
● frequently depend upon the **reactivity series** *(see page 60)*

the main types of chemical reaction are

● **oxidation** – chemically combining an element with oxygen to form an oxide (a compound)

e.g. magnesium + oxygen ⟶ magnesium oxide

● **tarnishing** of metals by the action of other substances such as oxygen and water to form a layer of compound – usually an oxide

♦ aluminium (a normally reactive metal) very quickly oxidises on the surface and this layer of oxide then stops further corrosion

♦ the **rusting** of iron and steel may be prevented by

– **galvanising**: coating with zinc which oxidises quickly to form a protective layer

– coating with tin, which is resistant to attack by acids, e.g. in fruit juices

– painting

– covering with plastic

– covering with oil or grease

● **oxidation** and **reduction**

e.g. iron + copper oxide ⟶ copper + iron oxide

iron is more reactive than copper; the iron has been **oxidised**; the copper oxide has been **reduced**

- **decomposition** – breaking up a compound into simpler substances, usually by heating

  e.g. copper carbonate $\longrightarrow$ copper oxide + carbon dioxide

- **reactions involving acids**

  ◆ acid + base (or alkali) $\longrightarrow$ salt + water
  (neutralisation)

  ◆ acid + metal $\longrightarrow$ salt + hydrogen

  ◆ acid + carbonate $\longrightarrow$ salt + carbon dioxide + water

- **displacement** – a metal displaces another from a solution of its salt

  e.g. iron + copper sulphate $\longrightarrow$ copper + iron sulphate

■ Extraction of metals

- an **ore** is a rock (a mixture of minerals) or mineral which contains the metal – usually in a compound

- the metal can be extracted by

  ◆ heating (**decomposition**)

    e.g. silver oxide $\longrightarrow$ silver + oxygen

  ◆ heating with carbon (**reduction** – the carbon replaces the metal)

    e.g. iron oxide + carbon $\longrightarrow$ iron + oxides of carbon

  ◆ **electrolysis** – using a molten compound or a solution of the compound

    e.g. aluminium oxide $\longrightarrow$ aluminium + oxygen

    the metal moves to the negative electrode; the other 'parts' move to the positive electrode

4. PHYSICS

4.1 ELECTRICITY AND MAGNETISM

■ Atoms

- an **atom** is the smallest part of an element
- each element has its own type of atom
- an atom consists of
  - ♦ a **nucleus** containing a number of **neutrons** (carrying no charge) and **protons** (carrying a **positive** charge)
  - ♦ a number of **electrons** (carrying a **negative** charge), equal in number to the number of protons, surrounding the nucleus

■ Static electricity

- can be generated by rubbing certain non-conductor materials against other materials
  - ♦ some of the electrons are 'pulled' from one material to the other
  - ♦ the build up of electrons (negative charge) may stay in place for a relatively short time but will gradually 'leak away' through the air etc.
- given a suitable **conductor**
  - ♦ the charges can move from one place to another very rapidly, often as a flash, e.g. lightning, pulling a nylon shirt off rapidly
  - ♦ the **discharge** is too rapid and unpredictable to be useful but it can give an electric shock and, particularly in the case of lightning, can be dangerous!

■ Electric current

This is a very useful and convenient way of using **electrical energy** (electricity).

- can be **generated** by
  - ◆ burning **fossil fuels** (chemical energy)
  - ◆ harnessing **solar** energy, **wind** energy, **tidal** energy, **river** energy, **geothermal** energy, **nuclear** energy and other forms
- can be **changed** into other forms of energy
- can flow from one place to another by cables and wires

■ Circuits

These consist of **components** connected by copper **wires**.

- **connecting wires**
  - ◆ are made of copper (good conductor) covered with plastic (good insulator)
  - ◆ do offer resistance – usually not noticeable unless they are very long!
  - ◆ may be joined to form a T-junction   or ⌐
  - ◆ may cross without contact of the copper
- a **cell** pushes electric current round a circuit
  - ◆ the **volt** is the unit of electric push
  - ◆ a single cell has a push of 1.5 volts
- a **battery** often consists of several cells
  - ◆ a 4.5 volt battery has 3 cells

- ◆ a 6 volt battery is represented by the symbol

- ● a **power supply** may be used instead of cells; the supply has **terminals**

- ● a **component** in a circuit

  - ◆ slows down the current and is said to offer **resistance**

  - ◆ is represented by a **symbol** in a circuit diagram

- ● a **bulb** slows down the current, converting electrical energy into heat and light energy

  - ◆ the filament wire is a conductor but not a particularly good one (e.g. tungsten)

  - ◆ the filament gets hot and, if it gets hot enough, it glows

  - ◆ if the filament gets too hot then it burns out

- ● a **fuse** is a safety device containing a thin wire which melts (in a safe place) when the current is too large; this breaks the circuit

- ● a **switch** can be used to 'make' and 'break' a circuit

  - ◆ a **single pole single throw (SPST) switch** is either closed (on) or open (off)

  - *◆ a **single pole double throw (SPDT) switch** allows a choice of circuits

  - ◆ a **push-button switch** is pressed to make the contact and then pressed again to break the contact (used in some desk lamps)

  - ◆ a **spring-return switch** makes contact

   only when pressed (used in door bells)

67

- a **resistor** slows down the current (offers resistance)

  - a simple resistor has a fixed resistance

  - a **variable resistor** usually consists of a coil of wire with a sliding contact which lets the current pass through more or less of the coil (used in dimmers)

  - a **light-dependent resistor (LDR)** has high resistance in poor light and low resistance in bright light (used in automatic security lights and night lights)

  *- a **thermistor** has high resistance when cold and low resistance when warm (used in fire alarms)

- a **diode** allows current to flow in one direction only

  - a **light-emitting diode (LED)** gives out a bright light when even a little current flows (used as indicator lights in electrical appliances)

- a **relay coil** can be used to generate a magnetic field (used in electromagnets)

- a **motor** converts electrical energy into movement energy

- a **buzzer** converts electrical energy into sound energy

- an **ammeter** measures the current flowing

  - the **ampere (amp)** is the unit of electric current

  - in a simple **series** (single loop) circuit, the current passes through every component and is the same everywhere

■ Circuit diagrams

These show how the components are connected.

● series circuits

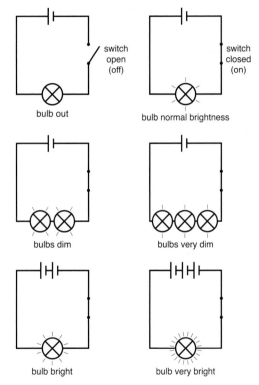

switch
open
(off)

bulb out

switch
closed
(on)

bulb normal brightness

bulbs dim

bulbs very dim

bulb bright

bulb very bright

- **parallel circuits**

  ♦ in a parallel circuit the current has a 'choice' of paths

  ♦ in a **short circuit** one path has very little resistance and all the current will take that path

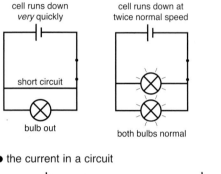

cell runs down *very* quickly

short circuit

bulb out

cell runs down at twice normal speed

both bulbs normal

each cell lasts twice normal time

bulb normal

- the current in a circuit

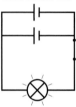

A_1 A_2

current in A_1 = current in A_2

A_3 A_4 A_5

current in A_3 is the sum of the currents in A_4 and A_5

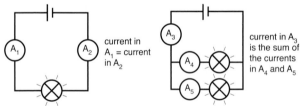

- **Circuits in everyday life**

- household wiring

  *♦ uses parallel circuits

  ♦ has fuses in the plugs of individual appliances, extension sockets and also in a main fuse box; some appliances have a fuse inside them as well

- Christmas tree lights use series circuits

■ Magnets and magnetic materials

● a **magnet** has a north-seeking (N) pole and a south-seeking (S) pole

● objects made of

   ♦ **iron** and its alloys are strongly **magnetic** – they are **attracted** to both the N and S poles of a magnet

   ♦ the metals **cobalt** and **nickel** and their alloys are magnetic but are not attracted with as great a force

● magnetic materials can be **magnetised** – made into a magnet

   ♦ a piece of steel which has been magnetised, and keeps its magnetic properties, is called a **permanent magnet**

● **lodestone** is a naturally-occurring rock which attracts magnetic materials

● a **compass needle** is a magnet which, when free to move, lines itself in a N-S direction because of the Earth's magnetic field

■ Magnetism

This is the **pulling force** between a magnet and a magnetic object.

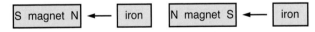

■ Magnetic forces of attraction and repulsion

If two magnets are close to each other then:

● unlike poles attract (pulling forces)

- like poles repel (pushing forces)

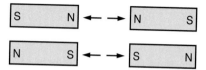

■ Magnetic field

This is a 3-dimensional region in which there are magnetic forces.

- the field lines can be 'seen' (in 2 dimensions) by

  ♦ laying a piece of card on top of a magnet and then sprinkling iron filings over it

  ♦ using a small plotting compass

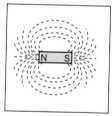 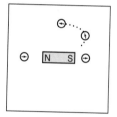

- field lines are considered as running from N to S

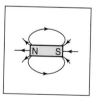

- an electric current flowing through a wire produces a weak magnetic field

■ Electromagnetism

- an **electromagnet** behaves as a magnet only when an electric current is flowing; it can be switched on and off

- a **solenoid** (coiled wire) gives a stronger field

- an iron **core** inside the solenoid produces an even stronger field (steel is less effective than iron, as it continues to be magnetic when the current is switched off)

- the strength of the electromagnet can be increased by
  - ♦ increasing the current
  - ♦ increasing the number of coils of the solenoid
  - ♦ improving the effectiveness of the core

- electromagnets have many uses, including
  - ♦ separating metals in recycling
  - ♦ electric bells

4.2 FORCES AND MOTION

■ Force

A force

- is either a **push** or a **pull**

- acts in a particular direction

- can change the shape of an object

- can change the direction in which an object is moving

- can make a stationary object start to move

- can change the speed at which something is moving

- can resist movement

- can stop a moving object

■ Effect of a force

The effect of a force in linear motion depends upon:

- its **strength** (size)

- its **direction**

■ Measurement of a force

A force can be measured with a **forcemeter** (**newtonmeter**) which contains a spring which is **stretched** by the force (or, less commonly, compressed)

- the larger the force, the greater the stretch

- the unit of force is the **newton** (N)

    ♦ at the surface of the Earth, a mass of 1 kilogram will stretch the spring in a **spring balance** (a forcemeter) with a force of about 10 newtons

    ♦ a girl of mass 40 kg has a **weight** (the downward force due to gravity) of about 400 newtons

■ Hooke's Law

- Within the elastic limit of a spring, the extension is directly proportional to the force applied.

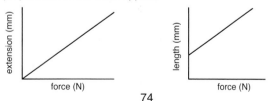

- The elastic limit is the point beyond which permanent damage is done to the spring so that it will not return to its original length when the force is removed.

■ Electrostatic forces *(see also page 65)*

These

- are produced by **positive charges** (shortage of electrons) or **negative charges** (build up of electrons)

- are usually small and difficult to measure

- can be a pull (**attraction**) between a charged object and an uncharged object

- can be a pull between two oppositely charged objects

- can be a push between two objects with the same charge

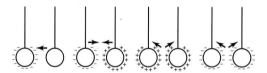

■ Magnetic forces

(see page 71)

■ Gravitational forces

- exist between all objects – but because the Earth is so massive, all other gravitational forces are insignificant

- depend upon the **masses** of the objects

- depend upon the **closeness** of the objects

- the weight of an object depends upon
  - ♦ its **mass**
  - ♦ the **distance** from the centre of the Earth
- an astronaut in his kit with total mass 240 kg on Earth
  - ♦ will have a weight of about 2400 N on Earth
  - ♦ will have a weight of about 400 N on Moon
  - ♦ may be **weightless** in space

  but his mass will not change!
- **overcoming Earth's gravitational pull**
  under normal circumstances an object will fall until it hits the solid surface of Earth but this may be overcome by
  - ♦ the object resting on (or being suspended from) something which exerts a **reaction (support) force** which is equal and opposite to the force of gravity
  - ♦ the object floating on water (or another liquid) which exerts an **upthrust force**
  - ♦ the object being propelled by a rocket (or some other device) which exerts a **thrust force** which pushes the object against the force of gravity

■ **'Driving' forces**

These can be produced by

- engines, burning fossil fuels (as in a car) or using electrical energy (as in an electric train etc.)
- human activity (as in pedalling a bicycle)
- natural activity (such as wind)

■ **Forces which oppose motion**

These include

- air resistance
- water resistance
- friction

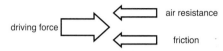

- **friction**
    - is caused by the roughness of objects (even if the roughness cannot be seen)
    - resists slipping – which is usually helpful
    - slows down moving objects – which is usually unhelpful
    - generates heat – which may be helpful or unhelpful
    - may be reduced by polishing the surfaces in contact or putting a film of oil (a **lubricant**) between the surfaces
- **air resistance** and **water resistance** may be reduced by **streamlining**

■ Balanced and unbalanced forces

- if forces are **balanced**
    - a moving object keeps moving at the same speed
    - a stationary object does not move

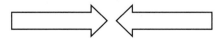

- if forces are **unbalanced**
    - a moving object will speed up or slow down or stop moving

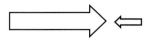

♦ a stationary object may start moving

♦ a moving object may change direction

↑ sideways push

■ Force and rotation

A force can have a **turning** effect called a **moment** (*m*) which

● depends upon

♦ the **strength** of the force, measured in newtons (*F*)

♦ the distance from the **pivot** (turning point), measured in centimetres (*d*)
if the forces are balanced then the moments are the same

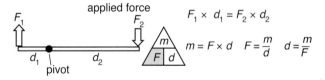

$$F_1 \times d_1 = F_2 \times d_2$$

$$m = F \times d \quad F = \frac{m}{d} \quad d = \frac{m}{F}$$

● can be very useful because a smaller force applied at a larger distance from the pivot can have the same turning effect as a larger force applied at a shorter distance from the pivot

● nutcrackers, bicycle cranks, scissors, levers, spanners etc., all make use of the turning effect of a force

■ Pressure

- depends upon

    ♦ the **strength** of the force (*F*)

    ♦ the **area** the force is acting on (*A*)

- can be **calculated** from the strength of force (measured in newtons) and the area (measured in square centimetres) giving a pressure in N/cm²

    *♦ another unit of pressure is the **pascal** which is the force acting on a square metre (10 000 cm²)

    ♦ a person of mass 72 kg, weighing 720 N, standing on two feet with a total area of 360 cm², will exert a pressure on the ground of about 2 N/cm² which is 20 000 pascals (20 000 N/m²)

$$P = \frac{F}{A} \qquad A = \frac{F}{P} \qquad F = P \times A$$

    ♦ snow shoes, skis and swimming fins have a larger area than feet

    ♦ the point of a pin is much smaller than its head

- **hydraulic pressure**

    ♦ is pressure exerted through a liquid

    ♦ is the same everywhere in a closed system

    ♦ can be very useful because a smaller area at one point of the closed system means that the force will be greater

4.3 LIGHT AND SOUND

■ Light

- comes from a **luminous** source, such as

  - ♦ the Sun and other stars

  - ♦ a meteoroid burning up in Earth's atmosphere

  - ♦ a heated wire (as in an electric fire or lamp)

  - ♦ burning flammable substances

  - ♦ some animals, e.g. glow-worms

- travels in **straight lines**

- travels at a high (but **finite**) speed of about 300 million metres/second

- can pass through a **transparent medium** (see-through material)

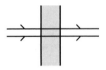

- can be **refracted** at the boundary between two different transparent media (one of which is frequently air) – it changes direction at the boundary

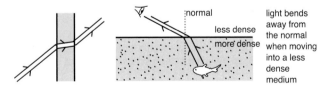

normal

less dense

more dense

light bends away from the normal when moving into a less dense medium

- can be **dispersed** (split) into a range of colours by a prism

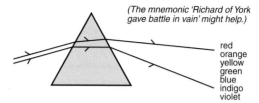

(The mnemonic 'Richard of York gave battle in vain' might help.)

red
orange
yellow
green
blue
indigo
violet

violet light is refracted to a greater extent than red light

- can pass through a **translucent** medium, but not very easily and the light which comes out is changed slightly – what we see is usually less clear

- cannot pass through an **opaque** medium

- can be **reflected** by all surfaces – anything that we see is reflecting light

■ Law of reflection

- when light is reflected at a surface, the angle of reflection is the same as the angle of incidence

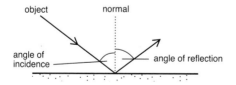

object

normal

angle of incidence

angle of reflection

♦ a white surface reflects all colours equally well

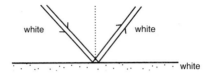

white   white

white

*♦ a red surface reflects red light and **absorbs** the other colours

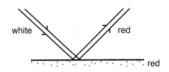

white   red

red

*♦ a black surface absorbs all colours equally

black

● a **shadow** is formed when an opaque or translucent object is placed in the path of light

♦ the size of the shadow depends upon the distance of the object from the light source

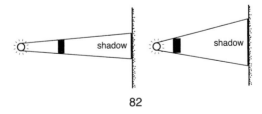

shadow   shadow

♦ the length of the shadow depends upon the position of the object in relation to the light source

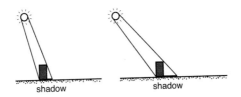

♦ a sundial makes use of a cast shadow

■ Seeing

We see things because of the light reflected from them.

■ Sound

● may be made when something **vibrates** (moves rapidly backwards and forwards)

● travels in '**waves**' of vibrations

● travels much more slowly than light – 330 metres/second (light travels about a million times faster!)

● from **musical instruments** may be from vibrations in

♦ a column of air – wind or brass instrument

♦ a string – stringed instrument

♦ a membrane – drum

♦ a solid object – triangle

but in most cases the situation is quite complex!

● **sound waves**

♦ can travel through solids, liquids and gases

- ◆ cannot travel through a **vacuum** (a space containing no matter – not even air)

- ◆ can be **distorted** (changed) when they travel through some media

- ◆ can be **absorbed** by some materials, e.g. sound-proofing

- ◆ get weaker the further they travel and eventually die away altogether

- ◆ can be **reflected** (echoes)

- ◆ travel better through moist air (over the sea or lakes) than through dry air

- ● the **volume** (loudness) of a sound depends upon the energy of the vibrations

  - ◆ **loud** – high energy; violent vibrations; greater **amplitude** of vibrations

  - ◆ **quiet** – low energy; gentle vibrations; smaller **amplitude** of vibrations

- ● the **pitch** of a sound depends upon

  - ◆ the **size** of the vibrating object

    - – **high** – thin string; short string; small column of air; small block of wood etc.

    - – **low** – thick string; long string; large column of air; large block of wood etc.

  - ◆ the **tension** of the vibrating object

    - – **high** – tight string; tight drum membrane etc.

    - – **low** – slack string; slack drum membrane etc.

  - ◆ the **frequency** of the vibration – the number of vibrations in one second; the unit of frequency is the **Hertz** (Hz) which is one 'cycle' per second; the higher the frequency, the higher the pitch

■ Hearing

- we hear sounds because vibrations reach the ear drum (a membrane) which starts to vibrate
- the vibrations are passed to
  - ♦ the bones of the ear, then to
  - ♦ the liquid inside the cochlea
- the cochlea sends messages to the brain

4.4 THE EARTH AND BEYOND

■ The universe

The universe consists of

- **galaxies** (groups of **stars**) which are generally moving away from each other
  - ♦ our galaxy is called the **Milky Way**
- **stars** which are spheres (balls) of burning gases
  - ♦ stars can be seen at night (when the light from the Sun is hidden)
  - ♦ the light (despite its high speed) has taken many years to reach us
  - ♦ astronomical distances are measured in **light years**
  - ♦ the nearest star to our Sun is about 4 light years away – the distance that light can travel in 4 years is about 36 000 000 000 000 kilometres

- **star systems** which consist of smaller spheres (planets and their moons) moving round the stars, held by gravitational forces

■ The solar system

- the **Sun**

    ♦ is our **star** (not a particularly impressive one, which is really good news!)

    ♦ is at the centre of the solar system

    ♦ is a ball of burning gases

    ♦ gives out the energy which warms the planets

    ♦ provides the gravitational pull which keeps the planets in orbit

- **planets**

    ♦ Mercury, Venus, Earth, Mars, Jupiter, Saturn, Uranus, Neptune, Pluto (in order from the closest to the Sun) and possibly others which are very small and/or very far from the Sun *(The mnemonic 'My very easy method just speeds up naming planets', may help.)* Note: Pluto is now classified as a dwarf planet.

    ♦ move in almost circular orbits round the Sun, except Pluto, which has an elliptical orbit in a different plane

    ♦ are kept in orbit because of the balance between movement (which would send a planet off into space) and the gravitational pull of the Sun (which would pull a planet into the Sun)

    ♦ the largest, Jupiter, has diameter about 143 000 km; the smallest, Pluto, has diameter about 2300 km

- **asteroids**

  - are large rocks mostly orbiting the Sun between the orbits of Mars and Jupiter; a few are within Earth's orbit and a few are outside Saturn's orbit

  - the largest is about 1000 km across; the smallest are very small

- **meteoroids**

  - are small asteroids which are on a collision course with Earth

  - get very hot (due to friction) when they enter Earth's atmosphere; most burn up completely and can be seen as a streak of light at night (shooting stars)

  - sometimes do not burn up completely; what is left strikes Earth's surface and is called a **meteorite**

- **comets**

  - are lumps of rock and ice

  - move in very elliptical orbits round the Sun

  - travel in orbits which take them very far away from the Sun; can be seen only when they come close to the Sun

- **moons** (natural satellites) which orbit some, but not all, planets

  - Earth has one moon, the Moon

  - Mars has two moons, Phobos and Deimos

  - Jupiter has four large moons and at least 60 smaller moons, some of which may simply be 'captured' asteroids

- **debris** which consists of bits of rock and dust

  planets, asteroids, comets and moons can be seen only because they reflect sunlight

  meteoroids can be seen because they become luminous when they enter Earth's atmosphere

■ Earth

- has diameter 12 800 km

- is about 150 million km from the Sun but the distance varies and Earth is closest to the Sun on about 4 January each year

- takes a year to complete one orbit round the Sun

- has one moon (natural **satellite**), the Moon

- has numerous man-made, artificial satellites which help us to

  ♦ explore the solar system

  ♦ observe and predict weather changes

  ♦ monitor man's activities

- has an average surface temperature of about 15 °C

- has an atmosphere of nitrogen (about 80%), oxygen (about 20%) and small amounts of carbon dioxide, water vapour and a number of rare gases

■ Day and night

(probably better referred to as **daytime** and **night-time**)

- are due to the spinning of Earth on its **axis** (an imaginary line through the centre of Earth, from pole to pole)

- one complete turn takes **1 day** (24 hours which includes both **daytime** and **night-time**)

- **sunlight** reaches Earth all the time
    - ♦ it is **daytime** for the side of Earth facing the Sun
    - ♦ it is **night-time** for the side of Earth away from the Sun
- the Sun *appears* to **rise** in the east and **set** in the west, due to the direction of Earth's spin

■ The seasons

- are due to the tilting of Earth's axis as it orbits the Sun
    - ♦ the angle of tilt is 23.5° to the plane of Earth's orbit

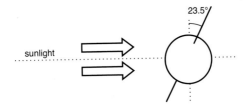

- Earth takes about $365\frac{1}{4}$ days to complete one orbit – so we have 365 days in most years but 366 normally every fourth year (leap year)

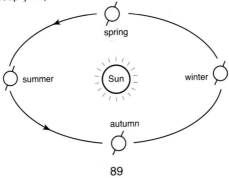

- in the **northern hemisphere**

  - **spring** – the North Pole begins to tilt towards the Sun; daytime gets longer; the Sun appears higher in the sky; daytime and night-time are the same length about 20 March

  - **summer** – the North Pole is tilted towards the Sun; days are longer than nights; the Sun appears high in the sky at noon; daytime is longest about 21 June

  - **autumn** – the North Pole begins to tilt away from the Sun; daytime gets shorter; the Sun appears lower in the sky; daytime and night-time are the same length about 22 September

  - **winter** – the North Pole is tilted away from the Sun; daytime is shorter than night-time; the Sun appears low in the sky at noon; the shortest day is about 21 December

- in the northern hemisphere, winter is colder than summer because the light from the Sun is less concentrated – it is spread over a larger area – because in summer the rays of sunlight hit our part of Earth more directly

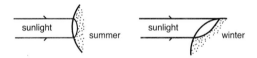

■ Moon

- the Moon's orbit round Earth takes about 27 days, 7 hours, 43 minutes (variable) (**sidereal lunar month**)

  - there are 13 lunar months in a year (13 × 28 = 364 which is close to 365)

- the Moon has
  - ♦ a side which always faces Earth but is not always illuminated by the Sun
  - ♦ a side which can never be seen from Earth (it can be seen only from space)

■ Phases of the Moon

- because the Moon makes one turn on its axis in the same length of time that it takes to orbit Earth, one half of the Moon is always hidden from Earth

- each part of the Moon's surface has alternating periods of about 2 weeks of darkness and then 2 weeks of light

- of the half receiving sunlight, only that part which is turned towards Earth can be seen by us

- when the Moon is in line between Earth and the Sun it is almost invisible; the whole disc may be seen only very faintly because of light reflected from Earth (Earthshine); this is the time of the new Moon

- it takes a **synodic lunar month**, about 29 days, 12 hours, 44 minutes (variable), for the appearance of the Moon seen from Earth to go through the sequence of **phases**

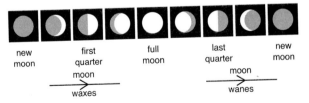

| new moon | first quarter moon | full moon | last quarter moon | new moon |

moon
→
waxes

moon
→
wanes

■ Eclipses

● in an eclipse, part, at least, of the Sun or the Moon is hidden from view by a shadow

● **lunar eclipse** – Earth casts a shadow on the Moon

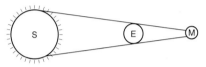

● **solar eclipse** – the Moon casts a shadow on Earth

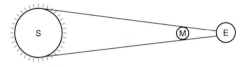

♦ in a total solar eclipse, the part of Earth in shadow is dark (like night-time) and cold because it is not receiving energy from the Sun

■ Tides

These are caused by:

● the gravitational pull of the Moon

● the gravitational pull of the Sun

● the rotation of Earth

4.5 ENERGY SOURCES AND ENERGY TRANSFER

■ Energy resources

● almost all of Earth's energy resources depend upon (or have, in the past, depended upon) the Sun

- renewable resources – solar energy, geothermal energy, winds, waves, biomass
- non-renewable resources
  - ♦ fossil fuels: coal, oil, gas
  - ♦ nuclear energy

■ Types of energy

- **potential** (stored) energy – needs to be released
  - ♦ chemical energy, e.g. in biomass, fossil fuels etc.
  - ♦ gravitational energy – things further away from the centre of Earth can move closer
  - ♦ elastic (spring) energy – elastic, rubber, springs etc.
- **kinetic** energy – energy of movement
- **heat (thermal)** energy
- **light** energy
- **sound** energy – is transferred as waves of vibrations
- **electrical** energy
  - ♦ is very useful and convenient in modern life
  - ♦ may be generated from a variety of resources
- **nuclear** energy

■ Conservation of energy

- energy cannot be created or destroyed
- energy can be changed from one form to another
- energy is **conserved** (not lost) in conversion from one form to another; it may be **dissipated** (spread out) but it does not disappear

- dissipated energy may be in the form of

  ♦ vibration

  ♦ heat

  ♦ sound

- a machine with high **efficiency** does not waste energy – as much as possible of the energy is used for the desired purpose

■ Measurement of energy

- the **Joule** (J) is the basic unit but, since this is a very small amount of energy, we use the larger unit **kiloJoule** (**kJ**) which is 1000 Joules

  ♦ lifting a tin of baked beans from the floor to a table top, will use about 3 J of energy

  ♦ running 100 metres will use about 8 kJ (8000 Joules)

  ♦ eating a bag of crisps will provide about 500 kJ

  ♦ eating a tin of baked beans will provide about 1500 kJ

■ Transfer of energy

Energy can be transferred (moved from one place to another) by

- **conduction** by particles – usually in a solid but also in a liquid

  ♦ vibrations are passed on without the particles necessarily moving

  ♦ energy is transferred from an area at higher **temperature** to an area at lower temperature

  ♦ metals are good **conductors** (plastic, glass and water are **insulators**; poor conductors)

- **convection** by particles (in a liquid or gas)
  - ♦ particles with greater energy move
  - ♦ warm air rises
  - ♦ convection currents cause winds
- **evaporation** by particles (the material changes state from liquid to gas due to the extra energy of the particles)
  - ♦ to break free from a water surface, water molecules need extra energy which is taken from the surroundings, making the surroundings cooler
- **radiation** (not by particles!)
  energy from the Sun reaches Earth by radiation
  - ♦ light rays which we can see
  - ♦ infrared rays (beyond red in the spectrum) which we cannot see
  - ♦ ultraviolet rays (beyond violet in the spectrum) which we cannot see
  - ♦ all these rays cause heating
  - ♦ all hot objects give off heat (thermal) radiation
  - ♦ the elements (bars) of an electric radiator radiate energy
  - ♦ white or silvery surfaces are poor radiators and poor absorbers of radiation, but they are good at reflecting it!
  - ♦ black surfaces are good radiators and good absorbers of radiation